# *The Breakup Workbook:*

## *A Common Sense Guide to Getting Over Your Ex.*

Design by Jonathan L. Day

ISBN 10-Digit: 0615279732
ISBN 13-Digit: 978-0-615-27973-2

Published in the United States.
PRINTED IN THE UNITED STATES OF AMERICA

For Kristy, Maricar, Cynthia and Christina.

And for Jim P., who was there from the beginning.


Thanks for always believing in me.

# Introduction.

I'll never forget the day that I decided to write this book. I was reeling from a breakup with my most recent boyfriend. I had been crying for days at a time, not eating and basically beating myself up mentally. I had finally gotten up the energy — relying mostly on reserves — to run some errands, and just when I was starting to feel a little bit "normal," it happened: I ran into another man (jerk) I used to date at the grocery store.

We had an awkward conversation at best and only because he approached me. He asked how I was doing and if I was dating someone — well you know how it goes. When I told him that I wasn't seeing anyone, he asked me out on a date. This invitation was coming from a man whose last words to me were, "You are a great girl. I love hanging out with you. But you're not girlfriend material."

I asked him if his opinion had changed. His retort was, "No, but I'd still love to hang out with you again."

Nice.

I left the store that day feeling two things. One, I felt as if I wasn't good enough to be someone's girlfriend. Two, I felt like a piece of meat. How many times had men told me that I was pretty and cool, but not a "long-term prospect?"

Too many.

I figured that I needed some sound advice to get out of my funk. It was everything I could do to get myself out of bed and run errands — let alone show up to work on time. And so, after throwing a major fit in the car and cursing all men, I drove to the bookstore in hopes of finding a plan to get over my breakup and boost my self-esteem in the process.

I stumbled into the "self-help" section, half-blinded by tears, and looked around. I was just a bit paranoid that someone I knew would see me, so I grabbed a couple of books that looked promising and went to another part of the store. There, hidden amongst the stacks in the sci-fi section, I began to read.

I was sorely disappointed with what I found.

One book told me that I should just get over it. Another book promised that it would tell me the secret to getting over a guy within 7 days (yeah, right!). Still another told me how "fabulous" I was and as a "super, sexy fox of a woman" (or something as ridiculously descriptive), it wouldn't take me long to find someone else, therefore I should start flirting immediately.

Right. I felt about as beautiful as a sack of potatoes.

While I appreciated the encouragement that these authors provided, I felt like it wasn't enough. I mean, really, who cares about the advice a celebrity gives? How hard could their lives possibly be? All bills paid; all eyes on them; the ability to step out on the sidewalk and literally point to someone that will be more than happy to take them out that evening. What made them qualified to dole out advice? And who the hell uses the words "fabulous" or "super fox" in everyday conversation? I know that I don't.

Maybe it's a Hollywood thing?

In any case, while these books were entertaining, I knew that I would inevitably read them and just as quickly discard them. I'm the kind of person who needs to write things down and, without providing an actionable plan to get over my ex and conquer my self-esteem issues, these books would prove utterly useless.

I needed to find another way.

I drove home that day with purpose. If I couldn't find a book that would help me, I would find a way to help myself. I would come up with my own actionable breakup blueprint. Then, using my writing background, I would turn the plan into a book to share with others. I was already deep in a hole of despair, so I felt that I was in the perfect state of mind to credibly write a book about digging myself out.

And so began *The Breakup Workbook*.

I commenced polling friends, family members and neighbors that very evening. I tried to find the secret "breakup remedy," but as I suspected, it didn't exist. I did, however, identify a recurring theme in all the advice I received — time heals all.

At this point, I knew two things: One, I wanted to write a book that contained an actual strategy to get over a breakup. Two, I wanted to write it in such a way that it would take a lot of time to work through. If time healed all, then I would need to give women — and myself — a constructive way to bide their time.

And so I wrote.

I wrote while getting over my ex. I wrote while I went to therapy. I wrote while I spent the holidays alone. I wrote and wrote until I began to see the light at the end of the tunnel.

And eventually that light grew bigger and bigger until it enveloped my soul and mended my broken heart. I couldn't believe it, but writing in this book and working through the exercises within it <u>actually</u> helped me.

I figured that the logical next step would be to test it on real live people. I didn't want to write a book and just put it out into the world and hope for the best. That would be irresponsible and foolhardy. I wanted my book to help people. Hell, I wanted my book to be more than just a book. I wanted it to be an experience.

And so began *BrokenHeartedGirl.com.*

*BrokenHeartedGirl.com* would be an interactive resource for the emotionally devastated, the forlorn, the desperate and the abandoned. I imagined that it would serve as an extension of *The Breakup Workbook*, with a support forum that would further encourage women to seek advice, talk about their breakups and genuinely get the most out of the experience.

Through the website, I actively sought feedback about the book. I incorporated a lot of ideas from women just like you into the narrative. And I crafted and honed it until I felt it was perfect.

This is the result.

People often wonder why I wrote the book from a "we" perspective. And I always say the same thing: The book, although written and put together by one person, is the culmination of ideas from many people — thousands of people. I wouldn't have been able to write it without the help and support from website members and friends and family alike.

So while you read it and work through it, I want you to think about all of the people who helped forge this breakup plan. I want you to seek support and advice from the women on *BrokenHeartedGirl.com.* I want you to remember that you are not alone.

We are all here with you: wishing you well and holding your hand.

Feel better!

- M.J.

# The Breakup Workbook.

**Getting dumped sucks!**

There isn't any other way to put it. Yesterday, you were so happy you could practically skip to work. Today, you don't even know how to put one foot in front of the other. You thought that you were with a man that could be the one, the only — the answer to your prayers. Now you are only left with questions: How could this happen to you? How are you going to get through it? How will you ever move on from the man you loved?

Everyone who gets dumped asks these questions, but there's no clear-cut answer. There's no magical solution to heartache. Ask anyone and they'll tell you that it takes time. So we wrote the book that will help you sort through your feelings while you take the time to get over your ex. And when you're finished with it, you should be able to understand why your ex wasn't as great as you thought he was and you will be armed with a plan to seek out a healthy relationship in lieu of repeating old patterns.

Like everything in life, getting over someone is a process. You've probably heard that it's similar to the grieving process - and it is. You're going to experience a battery of emotions: remorse, denial, anger, depression, hysteria, and at times you may even believe that you're going crazy. But to put it in perspective, getting dumped certainly isn't as bad as if someone you love actually passes away. Right?

Understand that, like the grieving process, you'll go from staring into space and bursting into tears to screaming at the top of your lungs and throwing things across the room. But invariably, all of these emotions are going to help you heal. So, no matter how silly or embarrassed you may feel, don't push these fits of rage or crying away. Embrace these feelings! Do the amount of screaming, crying, and yelling that is right for you. You'll know when the proper amount has been done, because you'll start to feel better.

**It could take weeks, or even months, but you <u>will</u> begin to feel better.**

We'll help you stay focused on recovery while you go through every emotion — from sadness and despair to eventual happiness. Staying the course and completing the exercises in this book could stop you from making phone calls to your ex at all hours, stalking him, or really doing something harmful to yourself.

We don't promise that by the end of this book you will be 100% over your ex. That would be ridiculous and presumptuous. But we can promise that if you use this book as directed, you will:

- Perform intuitive writing tasks that will help you to understand your breakup from a new perspective.

- Learn how to deal with the stress and anger from your breakup in a healthy manner.

- Discover new ways to repair your self esteem.

- Perform avoidance tactics that will help you refrain from calling, emailing, IM-ing or texting your ex.

- Learn how to take back your space and make your home your own again.

- Realize that you can write your own happily-ever-after.

- Ultimately view your breakup in black and white, accept it, learn from it, and begin to move forward with your life.

You may believe that you are going to extremes at times. But this book will help you understand that your feelings are normal and it will serve as a healthy outlet for your grief. It will also help you identify significant signs that the relationship wasn't perfect.

Work through all of the exercises completely — even overdo them. We helped just a little bit in some cases by filling out sample exercises to help jumpstart your thought process. We want you to thoughtfully complete each exercise in order. You may be tempted to complete the entire book in one night, but we strongly suggest you take your time getting through it — otherwise the book won't help and you'll still be stuck in limbo .

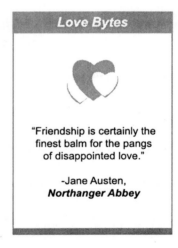

**Love Bytes**

"Friendship is certainly the finest balm for the pangs of disappointed love."

-Jane Austen,
*Northanger Abbey*

Take solace in the knowledge that you will get over him. But until then, do the work necessary to find yourself again, so that when you heal, you can take everything that's wonderful about you and put it into a new relationship.

# Exercise 1: Throw your own pity party.

So you just purchased a breakup book and the first thing it says is to throw a party. You're probably flipping back to the cover, wondering if you have the right book.

Don't worry, you do.

It's a party, but it's not the kind with streamers and balloons (and if so, black balloons would be apropos). This is your party. Solo. You don't have to put on a fake smile. You don't have to get dressed up. And you don't have to make sure that everyone else is having fun. Better yet, you don't even have to send out invitations!

**So what is a pity party exactly?**

According to a post on Urban Dictionary, www.UrbanDictionary.com, a pity party is:

"A way of experiencing grief, in which you spend your time feeling sorry for yourself and whining endlessly about how crappy your life is."

**So why should you have one?**

That's easy! To experience the full, unadulterated, horrible feelings surrounding the abrupt end of your relationship! In other words, allow yourself to feel exactly how you felt the minute he dumped you. Recognize your grief and embrace it. Then unleash it.

**So how do you have a pity party for one?** Good question. Here are some ideas:

- Turn off all the lights and close the curtains to set a dark, ominous, doomsday-type mood.

- Remove all of the liquor bottles and/or beer from your cabinet and mix some drinks (if you're of age, of course!). If you drink, don't drive.

- Cry. Every so often you can dramatically scream out, "Why me?" while shaking your fist in the air.

- Find every card he ever gave you and read them all out loud. If he has never given you a card, then curse him for never thinking that far ahead.

- Order take out: In fact, order the most fatty, tasty thing you can think of and eat it all without guilt.

- Read every text message from him (you know you have the sweet ones saved in your phone).

- Read every single email he ever sent you. If you're feeling ambitious, print them out and then shred them.

- Listen to every sad song on your iPod and sing them out loud - even if your voice is horrible.

- Review all of the IM conversations you have ever had with him.

- Watch sappy movies where boys do crazy stuff that never happens in real life (like stopping a plane on the runway).

- Throw your pillows against the wall to release physical tension (be careful not to break anything).

Keep in mind that there is no pity-party timeframe. Some people have a pity party for hours and some will have one for days or weeks. Just allow yourself to cry until you can't cry anymore. Don't try to be strong or ignore the pain. We know so many women that skip this stage and end up suppressing their emotions, only to unleash them at the most inappropriate times. The last thing you want to do is break down during an important business meeting or presentation. Just allow yourself to have this one moment of weakness.

And when you're ready and probably a little bit dehydrated, pour yourself a nice, tall glass of water and begin the next exercise.

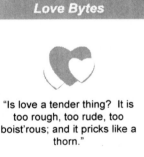

**Love Bytes**

"Is love a tender thing? It is too rough, too rude, too boist'rous; and it pricks like a thorn."

-William Shakespeare, *Romeo & Juliet*

# Exercise 2:  Realize that love hurts.

Hey, you're hurting. It's okay! You've just been told that you have to give up love "cold turkey" and it seems impossible to accept. And, unfortunately, for some people it can be. Love is like an addictive drug. When you don't have it, you crave it. You feel you need it for survival. You don't know how you can live without it (without him). And soon you'll start having "the shakes." This will come in the form of tears and anxiety.

Breathe.

While you go through this withdrawal period, subconsciously you'll magnify his good qualities. In your head, you'll build him up so much that you'll honestly believe that you'll never find another lover quite as good as he was. You'll never meet someone who makes you laugh as hard as he did. You'll never find someone as charming as he was. And you'll never meet someone that meets and exceeds all of your expectations, as he did.

To you, he is a man on a pedestal. And you will prepare to worship him in the days ahead.

So let's do the work to kick him off that pedestal.

**Really, how great can he possibly be if he doesn't realize how great you are?**

To heal, you're going to have to relive your relationship from the beginning. Although painful, these exercises will help you remember the good times and the bad. He is just a man who decided with or without your consent that he wanted to move on with his life. He is just a man — one man out of the thousands you could be dating.

Just one man. Remember that.

The next few exercises will seem to end abruptly. They are meant to gauge your feelings as they stand currently. Later in the book, we will analyze these exercises and prove that your ex isn't as great as you think he is.

So grab your favorite pen or pencil and let's get on with your journey. Start trying and you'll eventually quit crying. Yep. We not only want to help but we have silly rhymes too.

**List 10 things you loved about your ex:**

1) _____

2) _____

3) _____

4) _____

5) _____

6) _____

7) _____

8) _____

9) _____

10)_____

Examples:

1) He was funny
2) He co-founded a software company
3) He had a lot of friends
4) He owned his own home
5) He liked to travel
6) He made me laugh
7) He was a good kisser
8) He drove a nice car
9) He was outgoing
10) He liked to try new places to eat

# Exercise 3: Write the future that will never be.

Let's face it, you really loved your ex in spite of anything horrible or unforgivable he did to you. Even if you weren't exactly sure if marriage was in the cards, you probably had a few daydreams about the white dress; the flowers; the look on his face when he saw you coming down the aisle; the children you would have, etc. You may have even downloaded both of your pictures and morphed them together to see what your potential babies would have looked like.

Yikes!

So, let's pour all those wishes for the future out onto paper. Nothing to be embarrassed about here — nobody is going to read this but you.

We know this seems particularly cruel at this point, but the idea is that getting it down and getting it out will lead to a reinforcement of the fact that this hypothetical future will never be. Are you going to cry on these pages? Probably. But get it all out. Think of your tears as a metaphor for washing away the expectations you placed on this relationship.

**Write down what you imagined your future would be like with your ex — all of the dreams, the hopes, and the images you had of growing old with him.**

_____

_____

_____

_____

_____

_____

_____

_____

ACTUAL BREAK UP LINE:

I like you. I just don't want to date you.

ACTUAL BREAK UP LINE:

I'm Married.

*(Enough Said).*

# Exercise 4: Question your relationship.

So here you are at the end of your relationship and now we're asking you to go back to the beginning. What is this madness, you ask? Well, sometimes you have to go back to the start to understand the finish. And that "sometime" is today.

Travel back in time to when all things seemed perfect. If you find yourself answering any of these questions with a "but," it probably means that you're excusing some kind of behavior. It's called rationalizing.

For example:

Q: Did you have sex as often as you would have liked?
A: No, but he worked a lot and was often too tired. We only had sex once a week.

Hey, if you weren't happy with your sex life it's okay to admit it. Lots of people aren't happy with their sex lives. But if you weren't getting it as often as you would have liked, then it may be a significant sign that things weren't as perfect as you believed.

**So let's get to it. Take a deep breath and answer these questions about your relationship.**

1) How did you meet? _____

_____

_____

2) Where did you meet? _____

_____

_____

3) Where did you go on your first date? _____

_____

_____

4) In general, did he pick you up for dates, or did you usually meet him somewhere?

_____

_____

5) What about him attracted you the most? _____

_____

_____

6) When and where was your first kiss?_____

_____

_____

7) When did you meet his friends (how long into the relationship)? _____

_____

_____

8) Did you meet his family? _____

_____

_____

9) What did you think of his family? _____

_____

_____

10) Did he meet your family? _____

_____

_____

11) What did he think of your family (did he speak poorly of them)? _____

_____

_____

12) Did you sleep with him? _____

_____

_____

13) How was sex on a scale of 1-10? _____

_____

_____

14) Was he affectionate in public (or in front of his friends)? _____

_____

_____

15) Did you like that or did you wish it were different? _____

_____

_____

16) What did he do for a living? _____

_____

_____

17) Did you have any concerns about his job? _____

_____

_____

18) Who called more frequently? He? You? _____

_____

_____

19) Do you wish that would have been different? _____

_____

_____

20) Who emailed more? He? You? _____

_____

_____

21) Did you wish that would have been different? _____

_____

_____

22) Did he like your friends? _____

_____

_____

23) Did they like him? _____

_____

_____

24) Did he treat you differently around his friends? In a good or bad way? _____

_____

_____

25) Did he hold you after sex? _____

_____

_____

26) Was he reliable? _____

_____

_____

27) Who initiated contact more?  You or he? _____

_____

_____

28) Did he celebrate your birthday(s) with you? _____

_____

_____

29) Did you have to remind him repeatedly that it was your birthday? _____

_____

_____

30) Did he buy you a gift on your birthday(s)? _____

_____

_____

31) Did he ever buy you flowers or anything "just because"? _____

_____

_____

32) Did he attend your special events with you? _____

_____

_____

33) Did he invite you to his special events? _____

_____

_____

34) Which events? (anything involving his coworkers, family?) _____

_____

_____

35) Were you proud to be with him? _____

_____

_____

36) Did you pay for more dates than he did? _____

_____

_____

37) Did he support you financially or vice-versa? _____

_____

_____

38) What is the nicest thing he ever did for you? _____

_____

_____

39) What is the nicest thing you ever did for him? _____

_____

_____

40) Did he ever tell you he loved you? _____

_____

_____

41) If so, who said it first? _____

_____

_____

42) How long were you together? _____

_____

_____

43) Was your time together consistent?  Or did you break up previous to this? _____

_____

_____

44) How did you break up this final time? _____

_____

_____

Later in the book we'll analyze exercises 2, 3 and 4.  For now, move on to number 5.

# Exercise 5:  Avoid, avoid, avoid. Repeat.

A lot of breakup books stress that you should immediately and completely have no contact with your ex while you endeavor to recover from the breakup. And we, too, subscribe to that theory — with a caveat. We advise you to avoid your ex for at least the first two weeks after the big "B" day (breakup day). Then, after you've been successful, we suggest that you speak with him for the sole purpose of seeking closure. After that, you can continue on your journey to recovery.

I know what you're thinking: "Well, we said that we're going to be friends. I shouldn't avoid him. This, therefore, doesn't apply to me."

*Sure. You're going to be "friends."*

Ask yourself these questions and be honest:

•Do you only want to be his friend because you dream of getting back together?
•Do you only want to be his friend because you want to sleep with him again and wake up in his arms one last time?
•Do you only want to be his friend because you wish to torture yourself by listening to the gory and intimate details about his dating life?
•Do you only want to be his friend because you're secretly plotting your revenge?

Chances are that you said yes to one of these questions. Maybe you also believe that avoidance is crazy or just plain cruel. Fine. Be his friend like 6 months from now if keeping him in your life is that important to you. But if your sanity is equally as important, we advise you to stay away from him for awhile. If he asks why you've fallen off the face of the earth, just tell him the truth. If he really wants to be your friend, he'll understand.

It's not unreasonable to ask for space. If he gets angry with you over your need for time to yourself, then we suggest you question his intentions for asking you to be his friend. Friends respect one another. Hopefully he will respect your right to grieve.

A guy (yes, a man) on the *BrokenHeartedGirl.com* forum said the funniest thing: "Having the love of your life leave you and say, 'we can still be friends' is like your dog dying and your mom saying 'you can still keep it'."

How very true.

So let's focus on you. That's why you got this book in the first place, right?

Here are some basic avoidance tactics:

**Establish your support network.** First thing in the morning, call or email a few girlfriends that will support you — even if you're a crying, blubbery, neurotic mess. Let's face it: some girlfriends are like sisters while others are just "bar friends." Pick the ones that are closest to you and ask them for their help. Don't be proud. They are your friends and we're sure they will be more than willing to have your back.

Now tell them the plan: they are going to play defense against your offense 24/7, for two weeks straight. When you're itching to call him, you'll call all of them instead. When you're dying to email him, you'll email all of them instead. Their job is to simply respond to you and talk you out of it.

**Join a cyber support network.** When you sense you're testing the limits of your friends' good natures, log on to the forum at *BrokenHeartedGirl.com* and speak with other women whom are just as anxious to call an ex. It may help to speak with someone going through the same anguish. It'll help even more to speak with others whom are working through the same book. You already have something in common. We've broken the ice for you.

**Do whatever you have to do.** A support network alone isn't going to save you from your anxiety. A lot of people feel like they are going crazy when experiencing "ex-withdrawal." To some extent, everyone goes a little mad during this stage. Here are some tricks to help you get through the day:

• **Step away from the computer.** When you're at your wits' end and feel like you absolutely, positively have to send that email — even after everyone in your support network has tried to talk you out of it — take a walk. Like they say in the movies, "Step away from the gun!" Just get up and leave your desk. You can head to the water cooler and listen to some office gossip (always fun), or step outside and get some fresh air.

• **Log off IM and delete your ex from your buddy list.** As painful as it is, there's no need to see when he's online now that he's not a part of your life.

• **Write down the worst thing he ever said to you and post it on/near your computer monitor.** Every time you get an urge to make contact, read that piece of paper. It will hurt to read it, but those nasty words will help you realize what a jerk he can be — ultimately leading to the realization that he's not perfect.

• **Ditch the cell phone.** When you're at home and want to call him, go for a drive without your cell phone. Go see a movie without your cell phone. Go to a friend's house without your cell phone. Duct tape your cell phone inside a drawer and just check your voicemail messages from your home phone. Give your cell phone to a friend for the night. Donate your cell phone to the homeless. Just do whatever it is that you have to do to avoid calling or texting him.

• **Don't answer his phone calls.** Maybe he's trying to be the "good guy." Maybe he's just trying to sleep with you. Maybe he wants to get back together. Whatever his reasons for calling, don't answer the phone. Let it go to voicemail and after you listen to what he has to say, then you can decide whether or not to return the call. We suggest that unless he says he wants to get back together, you should just wait.

Chances are you'll call him back anyway and end up back at square one. But that's okay. It's hard to ignore someone when they are reaching out to you. Our point is, just be aware of his intentions and try not to place too much importance on the call.

• **Delete your ex from your Facebook and MySpace pages.** Then, stay away from his Facebook and MySpace pages and internet dating profiles (yes, we know you're glancing at those too). Checking up on your ex's "new life" is not going to accelerate the healing process. You need time to swallow the breakup and accept it. Internet stalking, so to speak, is not going to accelerate the grieving process.

• **Stay away from your ex's hangouts.** Perhaps they may have been your hangouts together, but right now that's all semantics. Avoid the bars, restaurants, the grocery stores, dog runs, and jogging trails he frequents. You don't need to do this forever. Just for now. If you have to drive an extra five minutes to go to another grocery store, then do it.

• **Go to lunch with someone else.** If you and your ex used to go to lunch together every day, start a new tradition. Maybe for the first few days, or weeks, you'll choose to cry at your desk during your lunch hour. But eventually, you'll get the strength up to actually eat. Call your friends and/or coworkers and institute a new lunch routine — one that doesn't involve your ex.

• **Invest in a timer.** Set it for one hour. Then clean the house, call your friends, read a book or play with your pets. When the timer goes off, see if the urgency to call him has subsided. If not, set the timer again for another hour. Record the length of time it took for the urge to pass. It could be 3 hours or it could be 20 minutes.

Do this everyday if you need to. Eventually the urge to call will pass altogether and you'll have a record of your progress.

Date: _____ Number of minutes it took for urge to pass: _____

Date: _____ Number of minutes it took for urge to pass: _____

Date: _____ Number of minutes it took for urge to pass: _____

Date: _____ Number of minutes it took for urge to pass: _____

Date: _____ Number of minutes it took for urge to pass: _____

Date: _____ Number of minutes it took for urge to pass: _____

Date: _____ Number of minutes it took for urge to pass: _____

Date: _____ Number of minutes it took for urge to pass: _____

Date: _____ Number of minutes it took for urge to pass: _____

Date: _____ Number of minutes it took for urge to pass: _____

Date: _____ Number of minutes it took for urge to pass: _____

Date: _____ Number of minutes it took for urge to pass: _____

Date: _____ Number of minutes it took for urge to pass: _____

Date: _____ Number of minutes it took for urge to pass: _____

Date: _____ Number of minutes it took for urge to pass: _____

Date: _____ Number of minutes it took for urge to pass: _____

Date: _____ Number of minutes it took for urge to pass: _____

Date: _____ Number of minutes it took for urge to pass: _____

Date: _____ Number of minutes it took for urge to pass: _____

Date: _____ Number of minutes it took for urge to pass: _____

Date: _____ Number of minutes it took for urge to pass: _____

Date: _____ Number of minutes it took for urge to pass: _____

Date: _____ Number of minutes it took for urge to pass: _____

Date: _____ Number of minutes it took for urge to pass: _____

Date: _____ Number of minutes it took for urge to pass: _____

Date: _____ Number of minutes it took for urge to pass: _____

Date: _____ Number of minutes it took for urge to pass: _____

Date: _____ Number of minutes it took for urge to pass: _____

**Practice avoidance at work** (yes, it's possible).

If you work with your ex, avoidance may seem hard, if not downright impossible. Simple advice is necessary in this situation:

• **Take time off,** if you can do it without jeopardizing your job.

• **Show up to work extra early,** so you don't see him or his car in the parking lot.

• **Change your lunch schedule,** so you can avoid seeing him at the cafeteria.

• **Don't give in to the company gossip.** Don't tell people what happened. When they ask, just tell them that you're "okay." Don't say anything positive or negative. That way, when it's time to seek closure, he'll be likely to agree to a meeting.

• **Be strictly professional** if you have to email him or call him for work reasons. The last thing you want is to get written up for calling him a jerk on company email.

• **Lean on your support network.** You'll really need their backup from 9 to 5.

To someone who is not going through a breakup, these avoidance exercises probably sound a bit strange. But when you're in the throes of anxiety, sometimes you just need help getting through the rough patches. We understand how hard it can be to act sane 100% of the time when you're going through a breakup. **So again, do whatever it is that you have to do. Just don't call him.**

You will be able to call him eventually, just not right away, and certainly not while you're so vulnerable.

**Love Bytes**

"When one door closes another door opens; but we so often look so long and so regretfully upon the closed door, that we do not see the ones which open for us."

-Alexander Graham Bell

# Exercise 6: Deal with his "stuff."

We're not going to lie. We really want to call it something other than "stuff." It's another word that starts with the letter "S," but it's only four letters long. Use your imagination and feel free to call his "stuff" whatever you'd like.

**Step 1:** Grab a box or a bag — nothing you'll need for the next few weeks.

**Step 2:** Go around your place and pick up everything that reminds you of him, every picture of him, every gift from him, and every article of clothing he left.

**Step 3:** Place every item in that box or bag. Feel free to look at every item and reminisce. Cry as much as you can during this stage, because when you're all cried out, we're going to need you to do some thinking. So get it all out now.

**Step 4:** Call one of the members of your support network and ask her if she'd mind keeping his stuff for you for a week or two.

**Step 5:** Get in your car and drive the box or bag to your friend's house.

**Step 6:** Give your friend a big hug and hand her the container filled with memories. Instruct her to keep the items for you and not throw them away. Tell her that you just need some breathing room, and it will be easier to heal without looking at these items.

**Step 7:** Stay there and hang out if you want. Talk to your friend as much as you feel you need to. Or go home and cry some more.

The important thing is that you don't call your ex-boyfriend. Even if he calls you, don't return or take his calls just yet. Seriously, don't do it. We know you want to, but stay strong. You have a few more exercises to go before you should call him or return his calls.

Yes, you read that correctly. You <u>will</u> be able to speak with him. So be patient. It'll pay off. And as they say, patience is a virtue.

# Exercise 7:  Make your place your own again

Chances are that everything in your place reminds you of your ex. This is the chair in which he liked to sit. This is the couch where you guys used to make out. These are the sheets on your bed on which you can still smell his cheap, drugstore cologne. Okay, so maybe it was expensive cologne and it smells really good, but the point is that it's going to be very hard to let go of him if you can still see and smell him everywhere.

If everything in your apartment, condo, or house reminds you of your ex-boyfriend, then the best thing for you to do is to change that. For most people, buying all new furniture every time a relationship ends is not an option, but there are some thrifty things you can do to make changes in your home.

**In the kitchen:**

When you think about your ex, you probably don't think too much about items in the kitchen. Well, my dear, that's why you got this book; we don't want you to end up digging around in the refrigerator three weeks from now, coming across a particular brand of salsa you purchased just for him, busting out in tears and ruining your progress. So let's take this time to get rid of those kinds of things. Throw away or consume any special food, beer, or liquor he used to keep in your refrigerator. And while you're near the refrigerator anyway, take down any pictures of him or love notes that you may have stuck on there. Finally, if you have any mugs or calendars that contain his picture – throw them away or put them in a box to dispose of at a later date.

**In the bedroom:**

The bedroom is probably going to be the harshest reminder of your ex. At the very least, see if you can move the position of your bed within your room so when you're sitting in bed, you're at a totally different vantage point. While you're at it, why not change the location of your nightstand or desk? Additionally, wash your sheets. We know that you want to keep 'his smell' on the pillow cases, but that's only going to cause you misery. You've already had your pity party. Let's keep moving forward, shall we?

If you can afford it, buy new sheets and a new comforter. You don't have to throw the other sheets and comforter away – maybe just put them away until it doesn't hurt so much to sleep in them.

**In the common areas:**

With the help of your more muscular friends, start moving your stuff around. Move the television, move your couch, switch the paintings from one wall to another, buy some artificial trees, install tract lighting; do whatever you can do to change the ambiance in your home without breaking your budget.

Take one more sweep of your home and pick out and remove key things that remind you of him. For example, if you and he used to curl up under a certain blanket on your living room couch, then put that one away and replace it with a different one.

Finally, clean up, catch up on laundry, and dust off your furniture. You can do all of this when you're not crying, and you can do it instead of wasting away in front of the television. You will feel better if you can mope about in a clean house. We know it sounds strange, but it's true. At least you will have accomplished something and that always feels good.

Right now, you are taking your life back from your ex. These small symbolic changes will help you make your life your own again.

If you're moving out of the home you shared with your ex (or even if he's moving out), then the same rules apply. Do whatever you can to jettison memories of your ex from your new place. This exercise should take you a few evenings. Shopping can prove to be therapeutic, but try not to overspend. You are depressed as it is right now. There's no sense in overextending your budget too.

# Exercise 8: Perform daily maintenance.

At this point, you're still avoiding your ex and you have a clean house/apartment/condo. You're still crying your eyes out every night and you're most likely smoking or drinking more than you're used to. It's perfectly normal, as we stated earlier, to embrace the grief. Take some consolation in the knowledge that these feelings of sadness will subside. It just takes time to get over someone who was a special part of your life.

**Purchase a journal.** *The Breakup Workbook* can be used as a journal, but there are only so many pages in this book. Writing in your own, private, personal diary can be a great way to unwind after a stressful day, or a fantastic way to start your morning. Write whenever you choose; just schedule time to write in it. A journal can prove to be a great outlet for your emotions. You can use it to doodle, to write poems, or to just plain write about how much you love/hate your job. If you choose not to invest in a journal, you can write in the "Notes" section at the back of this book.

**Perform the following exercise using the "tasks" pages at the end of this book, or complete the exercise in your personal journal:**

• Every single day, from now unto eternity (just kidding), write a list of tasks you want to accomplish the following day. These can consist of items such as successfully avoiding contact with him, allowing yourself to break down, promising yourself to cut down on the drinking or smoking, or even focusing on accomplishing a major project at work. The tasks can also be small: going to the grocery store, cooking a great meal, or forcing yourself to go to the gym.

• At the end of the next day, flip back to your entry from the day before and check off the tasks you actually accomplished. If you didn't accomplish a single item on your list, then that's okay. Just add these tasks to your list for the following day.

Accomplishing anything when just the idea of leaving your house seems daunting will help you feel like you're in the "real world" — even if it's just for a minute between sobbing fits. As more time goes by, you will find yourself completing more and more tasks. Writing it all down and referring to your list is a great way to track your healing progress.

**And for heaven's sake, eat something!**

# Exercise 9: Make an upbeat CD.

We know, we know. When you're in the car, you want to listen to your sad songs and cry, because at least you're not at home crying. Maybe you think driving around and crying is great because you can escape your friends or your roommate and cry in peace? Maybe you think it's great because you never know what kind of sappy crap you're going to hear on the radio?

Or maybe it's great because you have a CD and you can torture yourself by listening to "your song" over and over again?

We'll let you in on a little secret: it's not good to cry in the car. You're operating a vehicle that weighs a couple of tons. You may have pets, kids, or friends in your car. Maybe you're driving alone — but other people on the road have their pets, kids, or friends in their cars too. The point is that you have to be responsible while on the road, and if your vision is blinded by millions of tears and a runny nose is distracting you, then there's no possible way that you can drive responsibly.

And, really, do you need the stress of a car accident on top of everything else?

Here's what you can do to ensure that you're a safety demon on the road: Make yourself a CD or a mixed tape of empowering songs. Include rock songs, or old disco songs, or rap songs — it doesn't matter, as long as the songs are upbeat and they make you want to sing along. If you don't have the technology to burn a CD, we're sure one of your friends or co-workers will be able to make one for you.

Or, you know, they do have those new-fangled MP3 players that you can hook up to your car radio. That's another way to get the  job done.

Now sing at the top of your lungs!

And if you're in the car and you feel like you're going to cry — pull over!

# Exercise 10: Drive by the past.

While you're in the car, you can accomplish this fun little exercise:

Take a minute to drive by your previous boyfriend's house. (Not your current ex – the one before him). It may be someone you haven't thought of in years and you may think we're silly by suggesting this, but you've trusted us this far...so just humor us!

Try to remember how it felt when you guys broke up. Did he break your heart? Did you think you would never get over him or love again? Did you feel that your life was over when this relationship ended?

Hey, wait a minute? Isn't that how you're feeling now?

So, do the drive-by. Notice how it doesn't even faze you to be in his neighborhood? Notice how you're completely ambivalent as opposed to being a complete basket case?

Does this give you just a little bit of perspective about what you're going through now? It should. You went through this feeling before, you emerged and you rose like a phoenix from the ashes. You were strong enough to get through complete heartache before and you are strong enough to do it again.

Use the space on the rest of this page to write down the feeling you're having now. **How did driving by your ex-ex-boyfriend's house make you feel?**

_____

_____

_____

_____

_____

_____

_____

# Exercise 11: Write a letter to your ex (but don't send it).

You have now had a few days to calm down and reflect upon the breakup. Write a letter to your ex. You're not going to mail it or send it. This is just for you. Write down all of your feelings as you have them. Write down why you are upset. Write down what you want from him. Don't hold back. And if you feel as if you do need to send it somewhere, then post it anonymously on our forum at *BrokenHeartedGirl.com*.

You have our full permission to use curse words. We promise we won't tell.

_____

_____

_____

_____

_____

_____

_____

_____

_____

_____

_____

_____

_____

_____

_____

_____

> **ACTUAL BREAK UP LINE:**
>
> I'm sorry I cheated on you. I want to be with you, but I just don't trust you.
>
> *(Note the irony.)*

ACTUAL BREAK UP LINE:

I don't deserve you. You're better off
with someone that can appreciate you.

# Exercise 12: Take a relaxing bath.

Put the kids to bed. Unplug the phone. Get naked and light some candles. Strike that. Light some candles and then get naked.

Right before you're ready to go to bed, take a peaceful bath to help ease your troubled mind. Do this as often as you feel you need to. A psychic friend of ours said peaceful baths are helpful in cleansing the soul and they assist in washing away bad karma. And if you don't believe in psychics, then just take a bath anyway. It'll relax you!

**Items you will need:**

• 1/4 cup baking soda
• 1 cup Epsom salt
• A bath pillow to make you more comfortable. If you don't have that, then roll up a towel to place underneath your neck.

**Step 1:** Measure the baking soda and Epsom salt & put in the bathtub.

**Step 2:** Draw a hot bath

**Step 3:** Climb in

**Step 4:** While in the tub, think about things that make you happy. Concentrate very hard and visualize yourself being happy again. Your goal is to be relatively at peace when you get out of the bath.

**Step 5:** Remain in the bath for at least 20 minutes. After you get out, spritz yourself with some lavender oil if you have it. It has natural properties that have proven to be calming. You can also purchase lavender fabric spray and spritz your sheets to help you get to sleep.

**Step 6:** Got to sleep. You've earned it.

# Exercise 13: Break it on down.

Time to write some more. Sorry, but you need to get it out...It'll lead to catharsis and all that good stuff.

The letter that you wrote in Exercise 11 will no doubt bring to the surface some feelings you didn't want to —or didn't know how to — recognize before: anger, resentment, extreme depression, etc.

In the future, there may be some things you wanted to say to your ex, but failed to put it in your fake letter. It's like those times when someone says something mean to you and you can't come up with a witty comeback on the spot. You always think of that comeback later!

Well you don't have to write your letter all over again, We created a space for you to add addendums.

Use these pages as a repository: every time you think of something you want to say to him, write it here. Every time you have a notion of calling him, write here what you'd want to say to him. Use this instead of calling him. Carry the book with you if you need to. Feel free to tack on extra pages as necessary. You'll need to refer to this in a future exercise, so please attempt to make it semi-legible.

_____

_____

_____

_____

_____

_____

_____

_____

_____

_____

_____

# Exercise 14: Pamper your skin (without leaving the house).

We'll assume that if you're still staying holed up in your home every day that you're not wearing any makeup. Your face is either clearing up due to all the extra oxygen, or else it's breaking out due to all the extra stress. Either way, let's work on your skin regimen a bit. There's nothing wrong with being sad and showing a soft, supple and clear complexion while you're at it.

**Sugar exfoliant:**

- Grab your favorite facial soap and work up a lather on your face.
- Pour about a teaspoon of white, granulated sugar into the palm of your hand.
- Work the sugar into the lather using your fingers to rub the mixture gently in a circular motion. This will allow the sugar to exfoliate dead surface layer of skin.
- After a minute or so, use a warm washcloth to rinse the sugar and soap mixture from your face.
- Then wring the washcloth out and run it under cold water.
- Dab the cold washcloth on your face to close your pores.

And now you're ready for the next part.

**Facial mask recipes:**

There are many, many types of facial masks out on the shelves of the drug store - seriously, go to a store and count how many there are — it's overwhelming, but sometimes nothing is better than Mother Nature. Dig up some household ingredients and give yourself a facial.

**The original facial for any skin type:**

- Boil some water in a covered pot on the stove.
- Turn off the burner.
- Put a towel around your head and shoulders and let it hang around your face like a hood (so only your face is exposed).
- Use an oven mitt to take the cover off the pot.
- Put your head about 8 inches over the pot so the steam rises up to your face (do not get too close).
- Breathe deeply and allow the steam to naturally unclog your pores for up to 5 minutes.
- Run a washcloth under cold water and apply it to your skin to close your pores.

**Honey Mask for normal-to-dry skin:**

- Grab a washcloth and put it under some hot water.
- Put the washcloth on your face for about 2 minutes to let your pores open up.
- Place some honey on a napkin, a cotton ball, or even a popsicle stick and apply a thin coating to your face.
- Leave the mask on for up to 20 minutes.
- Use your washcloth to wipe off the mask.
- Put more cold water on your face to completely close your pores.

**Egg yolk mask for oily skin:**

- Break an egg into a bowl.
- Add a few drops of lemon juice.
- Grab a washcloth and put it under some hot water.
- Put the washcloth on your face for about 2 minutes to let your pores open up.
- Place some egg on a napkin, a cotton ball, or even a popsicle stick and apply a thin coating to your face.
- Leave the mask on for up to 20 minutes.
- Use your washcloth to wipe off the mask.
- Put more cold water on your face to completely close your pores.

**Banana Mask for Dry Skin:**

- Mash ¼ of a banana into a bowl until it's smooth and creamy.
- Grab a washcloth and put it under some hot water.
- Put the washcloth on your face for about 2 minutes to let your pores open up.
- Apply a thin coating to your face with your fingers or with a popsicle stick.
- Leave the mask on for up to 20 minutes.
- Use your washcloth to wipe off the mask.
- Put more cold water on your face to completely close your pores.

**Love Bytes**

"Man is sometimes extraordinarily, passionately, in love with suffering."

-Fyodor Dostoevsky, *Notes from the Underground*

# Exercise 15: Request a face-to-face.

The easiest breakups are with men who are not afraid to break up with you. He'll sit you down and tell you why he wants to end the relationship and then he'll offer you time to express your own misgivings — or to just sit there and cry. Or yell.

Some men can't get up the nerve to do that because they are afraid of the consequences. They don't want to hurt you, or listen to you yell, so they'll just email or text you that it's over. It'll make you feel horrible, but it happens all the time.

And some men, the worst ones, just fall off the face of the earth.

Even when a man breaks up with you "the right way," you may realize that there are some things that you still need to say to get on with your life and over the breakup. Part of you will hope for reconciliation and another part of you will just want to see him again. But most of you will just want to get the things you need to say off your chest. You'll be surprised how satisfied you'll be to get everything out in the open and say exactly what you feel.

Most likely, you're going to have to create your own face-to-face meeting with your ex. It may prove daunting to call him, but after two or three weeks of not contacting him, it should be "socially acceptable" to arrange for a face-to-face meeting.

The point of the face-to-face meeting is to be able to **air your grievances.** You don't need to be hostile. If you are, you may never get answers. So take a deep breath and remember that this confrontation will help you let go and move on. This face-to-face meeting will help you realize that the relationship is really over. Or maybe you'll both realize that it's still salvageable.

**If you don't want to meet him or see him, or if you can't get him to meet with you, all is not lost! Just skip to exercise 17.**

Here's what you do:

**Make contact.** Sometimes emailing him is easier than actually picking up the phone and calling him because all you have to do is read his response — not hear his voice. How you go about it is up to you and depends on your comfort level. But when you call, just be perky and upbeat. Most likely he'll let voicemail pick up, so make sure to leave all of the information on the voicemail. Tell him that you're calling because you have some things you'd like to say to him about the breakup. Tell him that you really would like to meet him face-to-face in order to make yourself feel better. Then suggest a place.

**Let him call you back to discuss the time and the date.** That way, he can't reject your offer if the date you suggest does not work. When he calls back, just calmly figure out the date and time.

**Don't talk about the breakup and don't linger on the phone.** Just finalize the plans, and if he asks how you're doing, tell him the truth. Tell him you're miserable, but you know that in time you'll heal.

Say goodbye and then run somewhere to cry privately if you have to. It may help to reaffirm your reasons for seeking closure. Write here what you hope to accomplish by meeting with him. It could be as simple as, "I want to meet with him because I want to be able to move forward with my life."

_____

_____

_____

_____

_____

_____

_____

_____

_____

_____

_____

_____

_____

_____

_____

# Exercise 16: Meet face-to-face.

**Prepare for your meeting.** Review your list from Exercise 13 — "Break it on down," and pick out key points that you'd like to discuss. Bring a list with you to make sure you have a chance to get all of your questions answered.

Take a deep breath, put on some waterproof mascara and head to the meeting spot. Be aware of your heart pounding in your ears signaling the fight or flight syndrome. Don't let the fear of seeing him get to you. Keep your appointment.

When you see him, you're probably going to either tear up, or become a rock of resolute strength. Whichever one you become, remember that you don't have to act like you're fine and that everything is wonderful. It's not. There's no reason to pretend that you have no emotions. Women like that only exist on television, and it's not healthy to deny your feelings. Just be yourself and discuss all the points that you wanted to bring up.

**Demand answers. Don't hold back (but don't yell either).** After everything the two of you have been through you do deserve answers to your questions, no matter how ridiculous he thinks they are. Remind him that these answers will lead you to closure. Chances are that he feels guilty about breaking up with you — even if he feels it was the right thing to do. Hopefully telling him you need closure will help him remain in his seat and listen to your feelings.

**Listen to him too.** It may be hard to listen to his reasons for breaking up with you, but if you don't actually listen, then you're not going to make any progress. Although difficult to hear, constructive criticism can prove helpful in future relationships. Even if you think he's dead wrong, make a mental note of his feelings so you can reflect on them in the future. Don't argue. Get the facts.

After the talk, there may be several outcomes:

**Outcome 1: You get back together.** If you're lucky, then both of you needed a cooling-off period after the breakup. If you're able to talk calmly and rationally, you may be able to salvage the relationship.

If this is the case, then still bring up your concerns about the relationship and try to see if you can work them out. If you can, then good for you! If you're comfortable with it, do what you feel is right in your gut. A good rule to follow is that in life and in love, you should always follow your gut instinct.

**Outcome 2: You don't get back together.** You'll talk and, eventually, you will figure out that reconciliation is not in the cards. If the chance to get back together is what you wanted, then it's going to really hurt when everything is laid out on the table in front of you. Hopefully you can get out of there and go home and cry. And hopefully the two of you will part civilly.

**Outcome 3: Breakup Sex.** Maybe the chemistry is still there and neither of you can resist! You sit there at the coffeehouse, holding hands and gazing into each other's eyes. Eventually you plan to head to his house to "hang out" and watch a movie, under the guise of "we're going to be friends now." You may be doomed.

Hey, maybe you'll have some mind-blowing breakup sex. But keep in mind that that's all it is. If there's one thing we've learned from the men in our lives, it's that guys think of sex as an activity — not as a spiritual experience. If you're "the best he's ever had," and he still breaks up with you, then the chances that he'll have a one-night stand with you or cheat on his new girlfriend with you are that much better. So are the chances of getting booty-called at 2 am. Either way, try not to give in. He doesn't want you back. He just wants sex. And if you do give in, then hopefully you're really okay with the fact that he may never call you again.

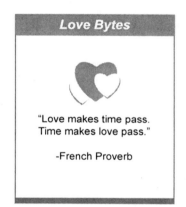

After the meeting, ask if you can call him sometime if you think of something else that you want to discuss. If he's a good guy, then he will say yes. Feel free to go home and cry if you need to.

Speaking with men after it's over makes it easier for you in the long run. It's probably because it makes the ex "tangible" and much harder to idealize.

# Exercise 17: Learn from the past.

You have just returned from meeting with your ex (or you were not able to meet with your ex, but still wish to continue participating in this book).

If things went as planned, then you were able to have a discussion with him and you were smart enough to abstain from sleeping with him. While the discussion is fresh in your mind, record your thoughts.

This is a pretty "deep" intuitive-thinking exercise. Take your time with it. It's important to thoughtfully complete this exercise so you can get the most out of it.

**What did you learn from this conversation about his perception of the relationship?**

_____

_____

_____

_____

_____

_____

_____

_____

_____

_____

_____

_____

_____

_____

_____

_____

**Do you agree with his perception? Why or why not?**

_____

_____

_____

_____

_____

_____

_____

_____

_____

_____

_____

_____

_____

_____

_____

_____

_____

_____

_____

_____

_____

_____

_____

_____

_____

_____

_____

_____

**Write down the things that you learned about yourself tonight (are you stronger than you once believed?).**

_____

_____

_____

_____

_____

_____

_____

_____

_____

_____

_____

_____

_____

_____

_____

_____

_____

_____

_____

_____

_____

_____

_____

_____

_____

_____

_____

_____

**What are some of the problems (in his mind at least) that contributed to the breakup?**

_____

_____

_____

_____

_____

_____

_____

_____

_____

_____

_____

_____

_____

_____

_____

_____

_____

_____

_____

_____

_____

_____

_____

_____

_____

_____

_____

**What are some of the problems (in your mind) that led to the breakup?**

_____

_____

_____

_____

_____

_____

_____

_____

_____

_____

_____

_____

_____

_____

_____

_____

_____

_____

_____

_____

_____

_____

_____

_____

_____

_____

_____

_____

**What do you think you did that caused him to break up with you? (Were you overbearing? Non-communicative? Overly sensitive?)**

_____

_____

_____

_____

_____

_____

_____

_____

_____

_____

_____

_____

_____

_____

_____

_____

_____

_____

_____

_____

_____

_____

_____

_____

_____

_____

**How do you feel overall about the conversation? (Hurt? Angry? Relieved?)**

_____

_____

_____

_____

_____

_____

_____

_____

_____

_____

_____

_____

_____

_____

_____

_____

_____

_____

_____

_____

_____

_____

_____

_____

_____

_____

_____

_____

_____

_____

_____

You wrote all of that down because we want you to remember this night very clearly in the days ahead. What did he say? Why doesn't he want to be with you? What's your reaction? You are going to have to read this over and over again, so that when you start idealizing him or exaggerating the events in your head, you will have a clear-cut version of the actual discussion. We want you to remember how he made you feel so that you don't spend all your time driving yourself crazy; thinking that there's nothing wrong with him or that he's perfect and he will take you back if you promise to change.

Recording your thoughts about the conversation was probably very rough, especially if you were brutally honest with yourself.

But now comes the truly hard part.

**You have to decide to get over him. You have to accept that the relationship is over. You have to make a decision to heal.** If you don't, then none of the exercises in the rest of this book will help you.

Take time to really think about letting go. Keep writing in your journal. Try to actually leave your house and be social with someone other than your dog. Keep your support network with you. You have to make a conscious decision to move on before beginning the next exercise.

You're at a crossroad right now. And a lot of times when faced with a tough decision, people want to invoke change in all aspects of their lives. This is fine, but whatever you decide to change, whether it be your routine or the kind of foods you eat, take this advice. Do not — we repeat — do not chop off all your hair as a symbol that you're ready to move on. If anything, go get a deep conditioning treatment and a facial at a good salon. Don't ever make hair decisions on a broken heart or an empty stomach. They may prove disastrous!

### Love Bytes

"In love, unlike most other passions, the recollection of what you have had and lost is always better than what you can hope for in the future."

-Henri B. Stendhal,
*French Writer*

**It's time to think really hard about letting go of your ex. Here's an idea for a journal entry. Answer this question: Why does your future happiness depend upon your ex-boyfriend?**

# Exercise 18: Seek help (if you need it).

We are not doctors, nor are we licensed therapists. Most women we do speak with are depressed in some form or another. Please read the following and seek medical attention if you are feeling suicidal, or the breakup is interfering with your everyday life — taking care of your children, getting to work on time, etc.

The **National Library of Medicine** describes depression as "feeling sad, blue, unhappy, miserable, or down in the dumps."

Further they say: "Most of us feel this way at one time or another for short periods. But true clinical depression is a mood disorder in which feelings of sadness, loss, anger, or frustration interfere with everyday life for an extended time."

If you are feeling as if you want to hurt yourself, or even worse, commit suicide, please seek help.

**Go to therapy:**

Call your primary care physician for a referral to a therapist. If you do not have a primary care physician, you can refer to the yellow pages or visit www.LetsTalkCounseling.org.

A lot of insurance companies now cover therapy. Some businesses have free counseling programs of which you can take advantage — and your problems don't even have to be about work! If you're in high school, you can talk to your school counselor. If you're in college, you can usually get free access to some form of counseling without paying a dime.

If none of these options are available to you, then use the internet to find free group counseling sessions (sometimes at your local YMCA or a local school), or you can ask a therapist to discount her rates for you. Some therapists will work pro bono dependent upon the situation.

If you're feeling suicidal, now is not the time to be proud. Just be honest and ask for help, or just go to your local hospital. Someone <u>will</u> help you.

**Call a help hotline (long distance charges may apply):**

Visit this website to see hotline numbers for over 47 countries —
**http://suicideandmentalhealthassociationinternational.org/Crisis.html**

US National Suicide Prevention Hotline: 1.800.SUICIDE

US National Suicide Prevention Lifeline: 1.800.273.TALK

US Depression Hotline: 1.630.482.9696

**If you're in immediate danger of overdosing or have harmed yourself, or are ready to do so, call 911 or an emergency provider right away.**

**Search for websites that will help you with your personal situation. Here are just a few:**

**For suicide:**
www.suicide.com
www.suicide.org
www.nami.org

**For depression:**
www.depression.org
www.stressgroup.com/depression
DepressionAndAnxietyRecovery.com

**For domestic violence:**
www.ndvh.org or US National Domestic Violence Hotline: 1.800.799.SAFE

**For alcoholism:**
Alcoholics Anonymous - www.aa.org
Alcoholism and Drug addition hotline - 1.888.268.9124

**Families or friends of alcoholics:**
http://www.al-anon.alateen.org/

**Drug addiction:**
www.ProjectKnow.com
Alcoholism and Drug addition hotline - 1.888.268.9124

**Families or friends of drug addicts:**
www.ProjectKnow.com

# Exercise 19: Start to repair your self esteem.

Chances are that after seeing your ex and finding out that you're not getting back together, you are feeling as if your world has been turned upside down. The little self-esteem you mustered before meeting with him has probably been depleted, and you feel that you have no reserves on which to rely.

But you can repair your self-esteem on your own. It will take a little bit of time, but you'll get it back.

**Say it out loud!** Grab a magic marker and some sticky notes and write down the following phrases – one per page:

**I AM BEAUTIFUL**
**I AM SMART**
**I AM POWERFUL**

Place these sticky notes on your bathroom mirror — or the one you use the most. Every time you see the notes, repeat what they say out loud. Even if you don't think it's true. Even if you don't believe it at the time.

And you should believe it! Every woman is beautiful. Every woman is smart. Every woman is powerful. You may not accept it now, but after you've used all of your reserves to get over this broken heart, you will begin to understand why it's true. Hey, you were beautiful enough for someone to fall in love with you. You were smart enough to keep someone interested in your intellect. You are powerful enough to get through this difficult time. You'll see.

Until then, repeat the words you see. Every time. Eventually, you will not only attain a better understanding of the phrases, but you will believe them in your heart.

**Visit the past.** If you have old love letters or emails from a man you dated in your past, search them out. Read them. Remember what it was like when you received these emails/letters and remember how good they made you feel.

Old love letters from high school are the best because they are usually so pure and full of love.

If you don't have old love letters lying around, then you can do the next best thing. Call either an ex-boyfriend that you are chummy with, or a close guy friend. Talk to him about the situation, the fact that you're miserable, and the fact that your self-confidence is shot. Most guys don't like to hear every single detail of the situation, so it's best if you just stick to the facts. However you tell it, your guy friend will be able to tell you what you need to hear in order to make you feel better. Good guys are always able to do that with relative ease.

A friend told us: "When I was getting over my ex-boyfriend, I couldn't escape him. He was on the local radio, so sometimes I'd hear him when I scanned through stations. Even when we'd go to the bar, I'd see him. It was terrible. I thought that there was no way that I was going to get over him."

"I mean, how could I do better than him, right? So I reached out to a guy friend to see if I was being completely crazy. And do you know what my guy friend said to me after a long talk?"

"No amount of money in the world is enough to excuse the way that you were treated. The next man you date may not be rich, and he may not be on the radio, but he'll certainly be better than that jackass."

That statement really helped her to remember what's important and it reminded her that her feelings do matter. She decided to spend time getting mentally and emotionally prepared to meet someone new — someone that would realize how amazing she is.

That's exactly what you're doing right now.

Here are some more self-esteem boosters:

**Do something you're good at.** Are you a chess master? A tennis phenom? Can you solve the New York Times crossword puzzle in under thirty minutes? Can you tie a cherry stem in a knot with your tongue? No matter how mundane, it has to make you feel good to know that there's something at which you excel. Do it! Then congratulate yourself for being so awesome.

**Shop.** There's nothing like a new pair of high heels or a tight pair of jeans to help you feel sexy and sassy again.

**Put yourself online.** You don't have to date anyone, but maybe just knowing that there are other people out there who would be interested in you — given the chance — is enough for now. And if you just so happen to meet a smart hottie, then roll the dice and go for a drink.

**Volunteer your time or give money to charity if you don't want to leave your couch.** There's an old saying that insists that to be happy, a person should do at least one good deed everyday. Some of us might only do one good deed per year, but just know that doing something is better than doing nothing. When you do something that matters to another person, you'll feel amazing about yourself. And hopefully it'll help you realize that in this big world, you can make a difference in someone's life. And therefore, you should realize that you matter.

**Take a few minutes and write down all of the wonderful things about yourself. Don't be afraid to brag. Go ahead and boast! Whether these are publicly celebrated qualities about you, or things that you just keep to yourself, write down what makes you special:**

_____

_____

_____

_____

_____

_____

_____

_____

_____

_____

_____

_____

_____

_____

_____

**STOP** Spend some time cultivating your self esteem before you begin to work on the next exercises. Remember, this book will not help you if you try to do it all in one day.

# Exercise 20: Write down the ten things you hate about him.

After the crying has subsided and you feel like you don't have any tears left, you'll notice that you're still not happy. Not only are you unhappy, but you're down right angry. You may not think of yourself as an angry person, but sometimes, anger is what can get you through the hard times. Anger can get you over the hump. Anger can help you get over him.

No examples here. Just write whatever you're feeling.

**Write down 10 things you hate about your ex-boyfriend:**

1) _____

2) _____

3) _____

4) _____

5) _____

6) _____

7) _____

8) _____

9) _____

10) _____

Now scream at the top of your lungs. Pounds your fists into a pillow. Take a long run. Do whatever it is that you have to do to get this anger out instead of letting it fester.

# Exercise 21: Unleash your evil thoughts.

Every time you're angry with your ex-boyfriend, with the situation, with everything, write down your feelings on these pages. Write down your revenge fantasies. Write down words you've only dreamed of using. Anger is an emotion that requires an outlet. It diminishes when you are able to get it all out of your system. Clearly, one exercise will not do it all, but writing down your feelings down will help. We hope this allows you to get it out without having to call and "go off " on your ex-boyfriend at all.

_____

_____

_____

_____

_____

_____

_____

_____

_____

_____

_____

_____

_____

_____

_____

_____

_____

_____

_____

_____

_____

_____

_____

_____

_____

_____

_____

_____

_____

_____

_____

_____

_____

_____

_____

_____

_____

_____

_____

_____

_____

_____

_____

_____

_____

| ACTUAL BREAK UP LINE: |
| :--- |
| It's not you, it's me. |
| *(Never heard that before!)* |

# Exercise 22: Create small goals.

When you feel as if you no longer have control over anything in your life, you will have to take steps to harness the chaos. Start by making a list of things you wish to accomplish and create a realistic plan to attain these goals.

**Write down 10 things that you want that do not include a man or a relationship.**

Some examples:

1) A bra that actually fits
2) Laser hair removal on my face, bikini line and underarms
3) A Range Rover
4) A personal trainer to kick me out of bed every morning (or at least three days a week)
5) An endless supply of ice cream in my fridge
6) A strapless bra that won't fall down or need readjusting
7) Perfect credit
8) Just one $800 pair of shoes, so I know what all the fuss is about
9) A well-deserved raise
10) A personal stylist, so I can look like I just stepped out of a salon, every single day

**Things that I want:**

1) _____

2) _____

3) _____

4) _____

5) _____

6) _____

7) _____

8) _____

9) _____

10) _____

**What are the steps you can take to get what you want?**

_____

_____

_____

_____

_____

_____

_____

_____

_____

_____

_____

_____

_____

_____

_____

_____

_____

_____

_____

_____

_____

_____

_____

_____

_____

 **Refer to this checklist often. Many people complain of being "bored" after a breakup because they don't have a man around. If you haven't completed everything on your list, then strive to finish it.**

# Exercise 23: Exercise, exercise, exercise. Repeat.

We're not telling you to work out because it will help you lose weight. We're not telling you to work out because it will help your self-esteem. We're not telling you to work out because it will help you focus at work.

We're telling you to work out because you need an outlet for your stress and anger.

We're telling you to work out because it's time to get off your rear end and back into the real world.

But, for added incentive: when you exercise, your body produces endorphins, or natural opiates that make you feel good. Exercise can trigger happiness, tranquility, euphoria, and creativity that will last from a few minutes to 24 hours.

So get out of your rut and start exercising! Not only will you start to feel better, but you'll definitely start to look better as well.

And while you're at it, ask a friend to work out with you. It's easier to stay motivated to work out if you employ the "buddy system." And, let's face it: it's more fun to scope out hot guys with a friend than all by yourself.

Take a moment to write down at least one of your exercise goals. For example you could write, "I would like to lose 2 inches around my waist," or "I would like to be able to run one mile without stopping."

_____

_____

_____

_____

_____

_____

# Exercise 24: Have a slumber party.

Invite your friends to your house for a sleepover. (If you feel you're too old for this exercise, feel free to skip ahead to Exercise 25). Now that you're not crying so much, it should be easier to have all of your friends around. Invite the person that has your box or bag of his things, and ask the friend to bring the items with her. It will be easier for you to handle the return of "his things" when your friends are around.

Make sure there's plenty of chocolate, ice cream, booze, and movies to fill up the night. This should be a fun occasion and the evening should not solely focus entirely on your broken heart (you already had your pity party). Allow yourself to have fun! You can have fun without him. We do realize it's hard, but you've got to remember what it's like to let loose and party without a man around. This is the perfect occasion for doing so.

When your friend arrives with the box or bag of his junk, excuse yourself and take it to a separate room. Find a few items that you would not mind losing forever and bring them downstairs with you.

If you find yourself crying, it's fine. Seeing his "stuff" (insert 4 letter word) again might be a little bit of a shock to your system. So when you're done smearing your makeup, get ready to get over the breakup! Yes, it's another trite rhyme. Sorry.

Just before midnight, ask that your friends help you perform a ritual that has probably been passed down for generations.

**Here's what you do:**

• Use a working fireplace or go outside and use a grill or fire pit.
• Keep a fire extinguisher nearby.
• Write down 3 wishes on a piece of paper. (These wishes are NOT for ill will toward your ex. These wishes are for you and for your future).
• Use scissors to cut up pictures of ex boyfriend &/or sentimental items.
• Place remnants of items into the fireplace, fire pit or grill.
• Take the bowl filled with the remnants and your wish list and step outside to the grill or fire pit.
• Place the ex-boyfriend remnants in the fire pit or the grill.

- Read your wish list aloud, then toss it into the fire pit or grill on top of the other items.

- Light your remnants and your wishes and recite this phrase (out loud in your head) as many times as you want, "I release my anger. I release myself. I release him."

- Watch the fire until everything has burned down, then put it out.

You can do this by yourself, but it's way more fun with girlfriends — especially if they bring their ex-boyfriends' "stuff" and burn it too.

In the exercise, we talked about releasing him from your life and letting go. This whole exercise was about creating and practicing a ritual for closure, an official way to say goodbye. You were able to let go of some tangible items, yes, but what else is left? **After your sleepover, make a list of all of the things you have to say goodbye to — waking up with him, telling him about your day, and more. Reflect on this list and cry. Let yourself go.**

**Love Bytes**

"A proof that experience is of no use, is that the end of one love does not prevent us from beginning another."

-Paul Bourget,
*French Novelist*

_____

_____

_____

_____

_____

_____

_____

_____

_____

_____

_____

_____

_____

_____

# Exercise 25: Dispose of his "stuff" one way or another.

After your girlfriends have left, you'll realize that you still have the remainder of his things in your custody and, that you may not be sure quite sure what to do with them all. Hey, if he's asked about his possessions, then the really cool thing would be to return them. If you don't think he wants his stuff back, then you can decide to throw it out, keep it, or give it to the Salvation Army.

Some of our best sweatshirts are from ex-boyfriends. But we don't wear them until we're sure that wearing the shirt won't hurt (another rhyme!).

If you want to keep his things, then just put them away. Put his love letters with your other love letters. Tuck his shirts all the way in the abyss at the back of your closet. And place the teddy bears out of sight for the time being.

If you decide to give back his property, make sure to email him prior to and tell him that you're going to drop by and leave his stuff on his porch. Ask him to do the same with your things if there's something that you really would like returned.

There's no reason that you should see him at this point. If you need to talk to him, then go back to your list of discussion points and see if there's something on there you forgot to address.

If you're still angry with him, write it down in your anger repository. As tempting as it may be to think of this errand as an excuse to see him, you have to reach deep down into your gut and abstain. You purchased this book because you want to get over your ex. If you don't follow the advice given, then the book won't help you.

**Dig deep. You can do this without seeing him. We know you can.**

**If you find yourself barreling through this book, then why not take a break? This book won't help you if you try to do it all in one day. Think about calling a friend or watching a movie.**

# Exercise 26: Phone a friend.

**Make sure you're ready to let go before you decide to work through this exercise. There's no coming back from it.**

Now it's time to pick up your phone and ask for some outside opinions about your ex. These assessments may lead you to discover some character traits you never saw in him. Ultimately it may lead you to gain the closure you need to move on.

The answers your friends and family members give may hurt you, but you have to promise yourself that you will not argue or swear at the people that care about you most. These are opinion-based questions, which means there are no wrong answers.

Some of your friends or family members may decline to work through this exercise with you. Be prepared for that.

**Call a relative and ask these questions:**

Did I seem happy to you with my ex?
Did you think he was good for me?
Did you like him?

**Now call a friend and ask them these same questions.**

It would be extremely beneficial if someone who has actually met him could answer these questions, as the responses will allow you to gain more insight into the situation. Call as many people as you think necessary to gain a consensus. Write all of the answers down.

**Person 1:**

Did I seem happy to you with my ex? _____

Did you think he was good for me? _____

Did you like him? _____

**Person 2:**

Did I seem happy to you with my ex? _____

Did you think he was good for me? _____

Did you like him? _____

**Person 3:**

Did I seem happy to you with my ex? _____

Did you think he was good for me? _____

Did you like him? _____

**Person 4:**

Did I seem happy to you with my ex? _____

Did you think he was good for me? _____

Did you like him? _____

**Person 5:**

Did I seem happy to you with my ex? _____

Did you think he was good for me? _____

Did you like him? _____

So. Was he really as great as you thought he was?

Even if everyone absolutely loved him, at least you know that you have the ability to pick a "good guy." This will help you in the next few exercises.

# Exercise 27:  Analyze it.

Refer to exercise 2 of this book. Read your list of "The 10 things you loved about your ex."

Dissect your list and see if any of the things you loved about him had anything to do with the way he treated you. We'll go through our examples first:

1) He was funny
2) He co founded a software company
3) He had a lot of friends
4) He owned his home
5) He liked to travel
6) He made me laugh
7) He was a good kisser
8) He drove a nice car
9) He was outgoing
10) He liked to try new places to eat

As you can see by the list, none of these items have anything to do with his character. Nothing describes him as kind, caring, attentive, sweet, or even trust worthy. If a person were to read this list arbitrarily they would deduct that he is an outgoing, funny, successful man that is a bit adventurous and a good kisser. It's doubtful that a person would deduce this as a list of 10 things she loved about her ex, because her list is superficial at best.

**Now go through your list again and see if you can gain any new insight into your attraction for your ex. Are the things you loved about him merely superficial? If not, then keep the good qualities from your list in mind. You're going to use them in another exercise.**

_____

_____

_____

_____

_____

# Exercise 28: Write the future as it really would have been.

What if you would have stayed with your ex? Knowing what you know now, how would your future have differed from the future you dreamed about in Exercise 3?

Some examples are: My parents would never have accepted him. He would have continued to cheat on me. We would have argued constantly and the foundation of our relationship would never have been truly solid. He never would have changed the demeaning way he spoke to me and therefore I would have always been trying to prove my intelligence. He never would have stopped beating up on me emotionally or physically and it would have scarred me more than it has already. He never would have stopped treating me like a maid and I would have spent all of my time trying to prove that I'm more than that. I never would have been able to help him or change him, because he has to decide to do that on his own. No matter the amount of effort I would have put into trying to help — he still would have to decide to change his behavior on his own. And he may never have changed.

Okay, those are a lot of examples. But we wanted you to realize that there are a myriad of reasons that your future may not have turned out to be as peachy as you dreamed it would.

_____

_____

_____

_____

_____

_____

_____

_____

_____

_____

_____

_____

Maybe I should have talked to you sooner about this, but I just don't think we communicate very well and that's a major issue for me.

*(So the first time you communicate with me is to break up with me?)*

# Exercise 29: Write your own happily ever after.

Lots and lots and lots of people forget to let go of the past when they are contemplating their future. But by now, you realize that you do have a future without him and the things you do in life actually matter in the grand scheme of things.

Plus, you have congratulated yourself on how awesome you are. Go ahead; congratulate yourself again.

Now let's focus on the future. **Write down your expectations. What are you going to do within the next six months to get over this experience, to learn from it, and to make yourself a better person?**

_____

_____

_____

_____

_____

_____

_____

_____

_____

_____

_____

_____

_____

_____

_____

_____

_____

# Exercise 30: Judge the men you choose to date.

You can blame men for everything bad that happens to you; if you spent a holiday alone; if you sit at home waiting for the phone to ring; if you are miserably lonely on a night when he canceled a date; if you are out at the bar and nobody asks for your phone number; if you are dateless for a wedding; if you are dateless for a work function. Go ahead. Blame men.

It is, after all, their fault. Isn't it?

No. It's not. And you can't play the role of the victim for the rest of your life. It's fine to console yourself with thoughts that men are evil, but after awhile, you need to own up to the fact that you choose the men you date.

Remember that you are not unlovable. Yes, men may not be all that great to you, but you are certainly lovable. Maybe the guys that want to be with you, who love you for who you are, are the guys that you always push away? Think about it.

Some women are attracted to alcoholics, some are attracted to womanizers, and some are attracted to deadbeats. Others are attracted to men that are hard to get. If you can figure out what types you're attracted to, and why you're attracted to those types of people, you can start choosing more wisely in the future. Once you figure out the code, you can use it to your advantage.

So let's do an exercise right now to figure out the types of men you tend to date. Then you can crack the code!

Here are some hypothetical men we have created to help you finish the exercise. We used a woman named "Missy" to help illustrate the exercise.

Man 1:

- Not college educated • In between jobs
- Very sweet • Very handsome
- Has potential to be financially secure

"Missy" will start seeing Man 1 because of the physical attraction. Eventually, she will start to care for him. When she begins to care, it leads her to want to "fix him." First she'll suggest that he finish his college degree while he's out of work. If he doesn't want to finish his degree, then she'll use her contacts to see if she can get him a good job. Eventually, he'll get a job because she'll push him hard enough and things will start going very well for him.

But once that man starts doing well, she would start to back off. As soon as the man started to become successful and as soon as he started to talk about settling down, she would start to think about getting out of the relationship.

And eventually, she would.

**Man 2:**

- Well Off • College Educated or Not
- Very handsome • Exciting personality
- Has unknown mental problems

"Missy" will start seeing Man 2 and everything will seem extremely exciting from the very beginning. This guy is always in the know, likes to paint the town red, and usually drives a fast car. If not fast, then definitely expensive.

These relationships generally last from two months to one year, depending on how quickly it deteriorates. She will be attracted to the "light" that the guy gives off. The sex is great, and then, somewhere in there, the light will burn out. Generally, the guy will break up, but since she's so into the guys that she dates that "Missy" will offer to be friends.

Through the friendship, the guy will tell her about his mental issues…either that he's on medicine, or used to be seeing a psychiatrist, etc. For some reason, she ends up wanting to "help" or "change" the person, and because of it, she'll become completely sucked in to the relationship — even though they are just "friends." Instead of focusing on herself and moving on after the breakup, she'll do everything she can to help these guys and to want to try and heal them.

These relationships caused "Missy" to try too hard and to be too available to the person she was trying to help.

"Missy's" synopsis is that she is attracted to men that need her. She believes that she has a strong mothering instinct, which causes her to take the focus off herself. She realizes after this analysis that she needs to find a man that is stable, reliable and can give her as much attention as she gives him.

Try this analysis yourself and see what kind of men you tend to date. Just write down qualities from the last 3 men you have dated. You'll be amazed at the patterns you will discover in the selection of the type of men you date.

**Man 1:**

_____

_____

_____

_____

_____

_____

_____

_____

_____

_____

_____

_____

_____

_____

_____

_____

_____

_____

_____

_____

_____

_____

_____

**Man 2:**

_____

_____

_____

_____

_____

_____

_____

_____

_____

_____

_____

_____

_____

_____

_____

_____

_____

_____

_____

_____

_____

_____

_____

_____

_____

_____

_____

_____

# Exercise 31: Set the standard.

What are you looking for in a man now that you know the types of men from which you should stay away? Make a list and don't settle for less than you deserve! If you recorded some good qualities about your ex in Exercise 27, make sure you include them on this list too.

_____

_____

_____

_____

_____

_____

_____

_____

_____

_____

_____

_____

_____

_____

_____

_____

_____

_____

_____

_____

_____

_____

# Exercise 32: Get out of the house! (this one is easy!)

The title of this exercise may sound like the title of a horror film, but it's supposed to sound like freedom. It's time. You have done all of this work. And you've done an amazing job. You may not be ready to move on to someone else just yet, but you can get out of the house and show off your new figure and see what it's like outside again. Some fresh air might do you good.

Whether it's going out on the town with your girlfriends, volunteering, or just going for a walk - here are some ideas to help inspire you to get off your couch and move forward with your life.

- Book a plane ticket for an exotic destination (with or without your friends) if you can afford it.
- Visit your favorite animal shelter and adopt that pet you've always wanted.
- Drive to Vegas with your best friend and don't go to sleep for two days.
- Go to church for services, or take part in a church event.
- Book an appointment with your salon: Get your nails done, highlights, or even eyelash extensions.
- Volunteer somewhere.
- Join your college alumni association and meet with the constituents in your city to watch a football or basketball game.
- Invite your parents to lunch.
- Go to your nephew's wrestling match.
- Ask your sister to join you on a shopping spree. She can help you find amazing clothes, but also keep you from going over your budget.
- Try to get your girlfriends together and hit the town. See a play, go to the bar, go dancing - even rent a limo! The world is your oyster.

In short, do whatever makes you feel comfortable within your particular lifestyle - and start living your life for yourself, not for your ex.

# Exercise 33: Learn to trust (and date) again.

We hope that after analyzing the rise and fall of your relationship, you have come to the realization that:

• Your relationship had both good and bad qualities.
• It ended because it was time for it to end.
• Neither he nor you were a perfect member in the relationship.
• The relationship is truly over.

We hope that when you are ready to meet someone, you will be as open and as trusting as you can possibly be. We hope that when you are ready, you will meet someone great.

Please use the forum on *BrokenHeartedGirl.com* to discuss any problems you may still have in relation to your ex, to yourself, or to your health. It's important to surround yourself with people who care and you'll find that nobody is more helpful than a person who understands exactly what you are going through.

**Before you go out in the world ready to date, we wanted to share with you some common sense advice:**

• **Get used to heartbreak.** Every relationship you ever have will fail until you meet the man you marry. Even after you get married, that relationship is not guaranteed to last forever. Invest in a nice fuzzy blanket, comfortable pajamas, a DVD library, and self-help books, for such occasions that you may need them.

• **Remember that dating is supposed to be fun!** It's not a job and you don't have to marry the guy just because you went on one date with him. Have fun.

• **Look your best everywhere you go.** Every time. Every place. It serves two purposes:

1). It greatly increases the chances that you'll get hit on while running household errands.

2). You never have to worry about your appearance when you run into your ex and his new girlfriend.

Either way, your self-esteem will soar.

• **Don't call, email, or text message your new beau until you've been dating for at least 2 weeks.** Just erase his phone number every time he calls. That way if he decides to fall off the face of the earth, you won't be able to make a fool out of yourself by calling a million times to find out "why." He's a new guy. Who cares?

• **If someone breaks up with you, remember that there's nothing wrong with you.** You just weren't right for him. Or any of the other guys you've dated. Repeat: there's nothing wrong with you. It happens to everybody.

• **Remember that some guys only view sex as an extra-curricular activity.** If you really want to be in a lasting relationship, think carefully before you sleep with your new beau.

• **Don't use sex as a weapon.** There are entirely too many circumstances to list here, but basically, don't use sex to get what you want. The only thing you'll get is immediate gratification, and a very large case of regret in the morning.

• **Remember that some guys really don't care if you're smart.** Some guys really only like you for your hot body.

• **Use a condom every single time.** No matter how cute he is. Not only will using one reduce your chances for getting pregnant, but practicing safe sex will also reduce your chances for contracting an STD. Buy a box of condoms and keep them in your nightstand drawer.

• **Remember how awesome you are.** If you meet a guy who doesn't meet your standards, recognize those significant signs. Don't allow yourself to keep dating the same type of guy over and over again.

• **Remember how awesome you are.** This isn't a typo. We meant to write it twice. If you meet a guy and he lies to you and cheats on you, don't ever put the blame on yourself. You don't deserve to be treated poorly. If the guy sucks, then walk away.

• **You are smart.** You are beautiful. You are powerful. Believe it.

Now get out there using your new set of standards and make sure the next man you date is worthy of you. You deserve nothing but the best.

# TASKS

_____

_____

_____

_____

_____

_____

_____

_____

_____

_____

_____

_____

_____

_____

_____

_____

_____

_____

_____

_____

_____

_____

_____

_____

_____

_____

_____

_____

_____

_____

_____

_____

_____

_____

_____

_____

_____

_____

_____

_____

_____

_____

_____

_____

_____

_____

_____

_____

_____

_____

_____

_____

_____

_____

_____

_____

_____

_____

_____

_____

_____

_____

_____

_____

_____

_____

_____

_____

_____

_____

_____

_____

_____

_____

_____

_____

_____

# TASKS

_____

_____

_____

_____

_____

_____

_____

_____

_____

_____

_____

_____

_____

_____

_____

_____

_____

_____

_____

_____

_____

_____

_____

_____

_____

_____

_____

_____

---
---
---
---
---
---
---
---
---
---
---
---
---
---
---
---
---
---
---
---
---
---
---
---
---
---
---
---
---
---
---
---
---

# TASKS

_____
_____
_____
_____
_____
_____
_____
_____
_____
_____
_____
_____
_____
_____
_____
_____
_____
_____
_____
_____
_____
_____
_____
_____
_____

# TASKS

_____

_____

_____

_____

_____

_____

_____

_____

_____

_____

_____

_____

_____

_____

_____

_____

_____

_____

_____

_____

_____

_____

_____

_____

_____

_____

_____

_____

# NOTES

_____

_____

_____

_____

_____

_____

_____

_____

_____

_____

_____

_____

_____

_____

_____

_____

_____

_____

_____

_____

_____

_____

_____

_____

_____

_____

_____

_____

_____

_____

_____

_____

_____

_____

_____

_____

_____

_____

_____

_____

_____

_____

_____

_____

_____

_____

_____

_____

_____

_____

_____

_____

_____

_____

_____

_____

_____

_____

_____

_____

_____

CPSIA information can be obtained at www.ICGtesting.com
Printed in the USA
239142LV00005B/113/P